S0-AIJ-739

Catch Me *if* You Can

The Story of Pinky,
the Sea-Wise Crab

Judy Brunk

St. John PRESS

This book is dedicated to my husband, David A. Brunk,
who introduced me to the Chesapeake Bay blue crabs
and his extensive knowledge of them;
to my sons Russell and John, who were watermen
and encouraged us to start a soft-crab-producing business;
to my daughter Paula, my first editor and writing inspiration;
and to my grandchildren, Walter and Kasey,
who have also learned to love and respect blue crabs.

In memory of my son
JOHN HOWARD BRUNK

Printed in the United States of America

Second Printing, 2010

ISBN 978-1-60530-747-3
© 2008 by Judith C. Brunk
P.O. Box 2, Jamesville, VA 23398
757-442-9030

All rights reserved.
No part of this book may be reproduced in any manner whatsoever
without written permission of the author except in the case of brief
quotations embodied in critical articles and reviews.

Chapter 1: Pinky Meets the Crab Lady

Pinky recalled his life as he hid in the soft creek mud under a boat. He remembered when he was only an inch wide. The ocean and bay were fierce, and only a sea-wise crab could survive and become a Jimmy crab. Pinky knew he had to hunt for food, find hiding places, and escape from many types of traps.

Pinky had been an ordinary crab until the last time he shed his outer shell. When that happened, he became a Jimmy crab, five inches wide, and he'd keep this shell longer than when he was smaller.

What made Pinky different—and what gave him his name—was that another sea creature—a pearly-pink shell—had latched onto his head. It stuck to his shell sort of cockeyed like a hat. A lady in a shedding house named him after he was caught in a crab pot.

Pinky.

After years of avoiding capture, he had let his guard down and been trapped. He had seen a she-crab and fallen in love. He had followed her into a crab pot and was holding her safely close to him when suddenly he felt a jolt as he was pulled to the surface of the water. Still clutching the she-crab close, he had been dumped into a basket.

A waterman with big yellow gloves put Pinky and his girlfriend in separate baskets. She was ready to shed, and Pinky would never see her again. Pinky had a

faint green color on his paddle fin, so the waterman put him in a large float with lots of other crabs. It all happened so fast that he had no chance to escape. Even a sea-wise crab like Pinky had forgotten to be careful when he fell in love.

The lady who tended the floats culled all the crabs every three or four days. Pinky was curious and swam up to her as she worked. He watched as she looked at the other crabs and either put them back or into another float. He sensed that she did not harm them, and he didn't fear her. He let her pick him up without trying to pinch her or get away. She always looked at his paddle fin to see which float to put him in. As long as his paddle fin stayed green, she put him back in the same float.

In a few days he found a new girl-friend and brought her to see the crab lady. Sometimes she let them stay together for several days, but eventually they were separated when his girlfriend's paddle fin turned red.

Pinky realized that if *his* paddle fin turned red, he was doomed. He'd be put in the float with the other crabs that were ready to shed. He'd become a soft

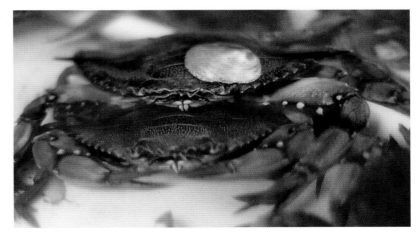

Pinky and his girlfriend.

Pinky's fate if he didn't escape— to be one of many crabs shipped to New York City.

Pinky gave up the shell with the pink hat.

crab and be put in a box and on a big cold truck for a trip to New York City. He'd be manhandled and shifted around until he landed on someone's dinner plate. He became frightened, because there would be no escaping this time.

Pinky held off turning ripe, or "rank" as the watermen call it, for nearly four weeks. Finally, he could hold Mother Nature off no longer. The crab lady picked him up and said, "Well, it's about time." But she also said, "We're nearly done shipping for the season, and if you hold off a little longer, I'll set you free." Pinky realized the crab lady had become fond of him because he was so curious and docile.

One day, late in May, Pinky felt his shell begin to crack. He was afraid, because the crab lady was still in the crab house every day, and she was still shipping crabs. He tried to hide among the other crabs, but the pink shell on his head made it impossible for him to hide.

He swam over to the crab lady with a sad look on his face. She looked at him and said, "You missed the last truck to New York, so I'll set you free." She put him in a big float all alone and waited for him to shed. She knew he would look just like all the other male crabs when he came out of his shell—no more pink hat.

6

About six o'clock that evening, Pinky came out of his old shell, and now he looked like all of the other crabs. Just as the crab lady promised, she let him stay in the float all alone until he was firm enough to swim and protect himself.

She got her camera and had him pose for a few souvenir pictures before she carried him down the dock and put him back in the water. He gave her a crab salute and dove under the boat. He was a full-grown Jimmy crab with all his claws and fins.

Pinky was grateful to the crab lady who set him free. He would always remember her, but she would never recognize him again because he no longer had his pink shell hat. He appeared like many other crabs except for the look in his eyes. He had the look of a survivor, a real sea-wise crab. He'd have stories to tell

Another souvenir picture before Pinky is released.

his grandchildren—about how he managed to become a full-grown Jimmy crab and still had all his claws and fins—quite an accomplishment. As he sat under the boat, he worried about becoming a white Jimmy crab. He would be vulnerable until he could fatten up and be strong again.

Pinky's first enemy— a great blue heron.

Photograph by Rose E. Taylor

Chapter 2: Pinky Escapes the Crab Trap

As he waited to regain his strength, Pinky recalled a time long ago when he was only an inch wide and had a soft shell. He had gone in close to shore and was hiding in the grass waiting for his shell to harden up again. He had seen a pair of huge feet nearby. It was Henry, the great blue heron. His mother had warned him about Henry, because Henry had eaten most of the other crabs who lived close by.

Pinky wiggled until he was buried in the muddy bottom. The earth shook as Henry used his large beak to snatch up crabs all around him. That was the first time Pinky had really known fear. By the time Henry left, Pinky's shell was nearly hard again, and he headed for deeper water out of the big bird's reach. Pinky had shed his shell several times that summer and had grown a little each time.

He remembered how lucky he was another time, when he had wandered along the shore looking for a safe place to shed. He had come upon a wire fence in the water and couldn't get around it. He kept working his way along it until he finally found an opening. He had crawled into a long funnel and seen several other crabs as well as some oyster-toads and eels. They were very excited and told him this was a trap—and *there was no way out!*

The trap was set close to the shoreline—along with many others—and there were many piers along the shore. Pinky was a sea-wise crab even back then, and despite what the others said, he knew he'd be able to find a way out. He began to search every inch of the trap, and after a while he spotted a cull ring. Cull rings are round openings built into traps to allow undersize crabs to escape. Pinky felt around, and after a struggle, he had managed to wriggle through the ring. He was free at last!

Two crab pots. See the circular cull rings? That's how Pinky and his friends escaped.

All the other crabs his size or smaller had followed him out. They were grateful to Pinky, a very sea-wise crab.

Pinky had spent that summer helping his friends outwit the crabbers and other sea creatures who wanted to eat them. After the great escape through the cull rings, he was treated as a hero by other crabs who were young and inexperienced in survival skills.

Chapter 3: Pinky Is Saved by the Marine Police

As Pinky sat thinking of his youth, he remembered how he had taught young crabs about the danger around the piers. He had taught them about the people living there and how they would set crab pots around the piers and dock their boats.

When the little crabs wandered too close to the piers, Pinky had told them about the time he spotted a chicken neck in the water. He had been very hungry and careless. He was eating the chicken neck as fast as he could when he felt a sudden jerk. *It was a trap!* He had been hauled swiftly to the surface and seen a little boy named Walt jumping in delight.

"I got a crabby, I got a crabby," Walt squealed.

"Yes, but he's too small, so we must let him go," said his grandpa.

Little Walt cried and begged to keep his little crab, but Pinky was lucky once again and as Walt's grandpa tossed Pinky back into the water, he heard the old man say, "We'll catch a big one next time, and then you can keep it."

Pinky had told the little crabs not to eat things too near the piers because most food around the piers was bait in a trap. He had escaped many times by sheer luck because he was too small to keep, but he knew there would come a day when he'd be five inches wide and be considered a keeper. He remembered the time an unscrupulous waterman caught him when he was about four and three quarters of an inch. The waterman didn't obey the law and return him to the water. Pinky was put in a basket on top of some other crabs and had many others thrown on top of him.

Pinky just knew this would be his demise. He had been overheated in the sun and had become very uncomfortable. He was about to give up when he felt the basket being jostled around. The next thing he knew he was being picked from the basket by a man wearing a shiny badge on his shirt. The man had held him by a back fin and laid a measuring stick across his shell. By now Pinky had become dry and weak. The lawman said, "This crab is undersize" as he tossed Pinky back into the water. That was as close as Pinky had come to dying, and it was an experience he didn't like to remember.

PInky had a very close call with little Walt at this pier.

Chapter 4: Pinky Leads the Pack

As he waited at the crab lady's dock to regain his strength, Pinky's mind wandered again back to the little crabs around the pier when he was younger. His stories had frightened them, and they had wanted to go to deeper water. Pinky led them all out to the channel, explaining to them that it was usually safe there. There weren't too many traps there, he said, but they must look out for eels and fish. Sometimes the only way a crab could be safe from them was to bury itself in the mud. Crabs had to be careful and suspicious all the time.

Pinky was slightly amused as he recalled leading the crabs to the channel. Heading toward the bay, they had seen several crab pots and eel pots along the edges of the channel, and many contained crabs, fish, and eels. The smaller creatures were squeezing out through the cull rings, but the others were busy eating the fish bait in the centers of the pots and didn't seem to realize they were trapped. The live fish, eels, and crabs were even trying to eat each other, but weren't very successful. It was sort of fun to watch, but scary too, so Pinky had urged his friends to head for the bay.

As Pinky and the other crabs had headed for the bay, he thought about the long trip south to hibernate for the winter. He knew there were lots of hazards between here and the hibernation place. Danger mostly lurked when he stopped to rest or eat, so he had to keep moving. He remembered all the friends he had lost because they were too hungry to listen to his cautions. Most had been caught in crab pots and were never seen again, but some were set free by honest watermen or the marine police when they reached the dock. Some didn't escape and had ended up in the steamer. Pinky shuddered at that thought.

With that unpleasant memory, Pinky settled into the mud and slept all night, and by morning he was a white Jimmy—still clean and fragile but able to feed himself once again. He searched for food and reminded himself how close he had been to being food for someone else. He would have to be very careful.

Pinky feasted on the steamed remains of crabs that had been tossed into the water after the people had eaten their fill. He stayed around the crab lady's dock, hiding under the boat at night. Each evening his thoughts went back to how he had survived so long and become a sea-wise crab.

Pinky stayed near the crab lady's dock eating and waiting to regain his strength.

Chapter 5: Pinky Escapes Again

Pinky recalled his first trip to hibernate in the rough seas. He'd had many close calls and escaped from several traps. One time in particular he had swum very deep in the bay and gone after fish with a lot of other crabs. As usual, the fish was bait in a crab pot and when it rose to the surface he had panicked. He feared there was no escape, but again, he got lucky. The sea was so rough that just as the waterman opened the crab pot, a huge wave hit the boat, causing the waterman to lurch and lose his balance. The crab pot flew out of his hands and back into the water. Pinky and most of the other crabs had managed to escape, and they dove to the bottom. The waterman quickly retrieved the pot and only the ones in the top had escaped. Pinky learned from that experience to always swim to the top and near the opening if ever caught again.

Another narrow escape for Pinky occurred when a wave knocked a crab pot out of the waterman's hands. He could have joined these doubler crabs and ended up as someone's dinner.

Chapter 6: Pinky Avoids the Dip Net

Several days went by, and Pinky still hung around the crab lady's dock. For some reason he felt safe there because the boat had not moved since he'd been set free. He had plenty to eat and was getting stronger every day. There were two crab pots in the water by the dock, but he was smart enough to stay away from them.

It was a hot, sunny day, and the water was still, but it began to churn and get muddy, and Pinky realized the boat was moving. He swam away like a shot and followed the boat to deep water. He saw a rope settle on the bottom and recognized it as a trotline. It brought back another survival memory.

Pinky was smart enough to stay away from this dip net.

The first time he had seen one of those was on his first trip south to hibernate. As he and the small crabs were moving along, he had noticed a few of them stopped to nibble on something. As he got closer he realized it was a chunk of eel. All crabs like eel and he was no different. He had squeezed in among the smaller crabs and was enjoying his meal when suddenly they all began to rise to the surface. They had all spotted the dip net at the same time and released their grip on the eel and the dip net had just missed them as they dove. Pinky had never before witnessed a trotline, but would not soon forget that one. As they swam back, they saw more crabs hanging onto the bait. Pinky had tried to warn them, but a few wouldn't listen. Some of the big Jimmy crabs had hung on and gone all the way to the top and never came back. The dip net had gotten them.

Some crabs survive so long that they become careless, but Pinky vowed he would never be dinner for anything or anybody. He was a sea-wise crab and a survivor. He had figured out that he could eat the bait on the trotline as long as he let go of it before it reached the top of the water. He could eat his fill and not get caught.

Pinky watched the crab lady's husband set his trotline, but he was full and decided not to eat any more bait. With darkness setting in, he decided to head out to the bay. He was constantly on the lookout for predators, because he could be someone's dinner if he became careless. He swam out to deep water and mingled with other crabs until the water glistened with sunset colors.

Then he headed back to the shallow water along the shore seeking shelter for the night and wandered until he ran into a familiar sight—some tires he had stumbled onto years ago. They had been thrown into the water by farmers hoping that oysters would strike on them. Oysters were attached to the tires, but Pinky was full, so he had decided to spend the night inside a tire and have oysters for breakfast. He felt safe, because oysters don't eat crabs. With his back to the tire wall, nothing could sneak up on him. This, he thought, would be a good place to stay again.

As he settled in he couldn't help but remember the time when a tire he was interested in was occupied. A buster crab had found shelter and was in the process of becoming a soft-shell crab. Pinky had been glad his tummy was full and he wasn't tempted to eat her. She'd be a sook (a full-grown female) after she shed. She'd become a mother crab if she survived and wasn't eaten by something or somebody. He thought about her more now that he was a full-grown Jimmy. Unlike the time before when he had been so young, now if he came upon a crab like her he would protect her until she shed and then become her mate. The other time he recalled a commotion at first light of day that had frightened him until he realized it was just a Jimmy crab trying to cuddle up to the sook, who had come out of her shell and was ready to mate. He had moved along to another tire and an oyster breakfast before heading south. As he was eating his oysters he had been startled by the sound of a dip net hitting the water and had became very still so he wouldn't be noticed. It was then that he had seen little Johnny, the crab lady's son,

The crab lady's son caught a sook and a Jimmy, but not Pinky.

with the sook and her Jimmy in his net. Little Johnny was so excited about catching them that he had run home without seeking any more crabs. Such vivid memories were what enabled him to survive. He never forgot an experience.

The next morning was much different from the one years ago. This time there were no oysters for breakfast. Nothing was as plentiful in the bay and creeks as in years past. Mankind was taking its toll.

Chapter 7: Pinky Finds a Mate

By now Pinky was getting back to being a big hard Jimmy crab with strong claws and solid body. He could take good care of himself. He was a happy crab. He was much stronger than he had been for the past few days, so he began to search for food. He found a few mussel clams along the shore, but the tide was going out, so he decided to move to deeper water. He could eat plankton and other natural nutrients in the water. but what he really wanted was fresh fish. Unfortunately, other than going into a crab pot he didn't know where to find such a delicacy.

Pinky walked along the bottom, observing all the activity of the sea life. He remembered when he was very small and afraid of all the other creatures. Now that he was big and strong, some of them were afraid of him. None of them were trying to eat him now because they were all busy just trying to survive. Pinky didn't fear too many creatures other than mankind.

Now and then he noticed a boat bottom overhead, some going very fast while others just seemed to be drifting along. As he neared the channel he noticed a small boat bobbing around. He swam up under it and found a few barnacles. *Pretty tasty snack,* he thought. As he was eating, he saw a fish being pulled to the surface. It was struggling and thrashing, trying desperately to get away. He realized that the boat above was a serious threat to the sea life below. He was glad to be a sea-wise crab and not a fish.

Pinky is now a big, hard Jimmy crab with strong claws and a solid body.

Suddenly the fish came back down. It had a bloody mouth and was obviously very frightened, but it managed to swim away. Pinky figured that it must have been too small or not very tasty to man. It was pretty safe under the boat, so Pinky went back to his barnacle breakfast. When his belly was full he moved out to the deep water of the channel, where he always felt safe. He passed many crab pots as well as cans, bottles, and other discarded pieces of junk settled on the creek bottom.

He was startled when like a flash, from the midst of the junk came a big she-crab. She rushed right into Pinky's grasp and snuggled up to him. She was very close to shedding. He held her close and carried her back among the pieces of junk where she had been hiding. There they relaxed, and other than a few passing fish and eels, they saw nothing of a threatening nature.

A warm, satisfied feeling came over Pinky as he held his new sweetheart close. He thought of the crab lady and was glad she wasn't around to snatch this girl from him. Now and then she would look up, and when their eyes met he thought about what a beautiful sook she would be. He was truly in love.

Pinky and his sook.

Just after dark her shell began to crack. By dawn it was gone, and the mating process began. The sook knew Pinky would continue to protect her until she was at least firm enough to swim and feed herself. She would become the mother of his baby crabs. Pinky was very proud to have been chosen as a mate by such a big, healthy six-inch female. He knew she would spawn a hardy bunch of offspring with such a sea-wise crab for a father. He gazed into her big black eyes and hoped she would stay close by him for protection until she was strong enough to protect herself. By the look in her eyes he knew her thoughts were the same.

Pinky was overwhelmed by contentment but was beginning to feel the pangs of hunger. He began searching for food while still clinging to his sook. They spent all day and that night together. By morning he knew it was time to let her go, but he was concerned for her safety because she would still be fragile for a day or two. Pinky wished they were back at the crab lady's dock under the boat. It would be safe there with plenty to eat.

As the sun became brighter, the water came alive with activity. Boats arrived, and soon the crab pots all around were being pulled to the surface. They soon returned to the bottom empty except for the fresh fish in the centers.

The sook broke free from Pinky's grasp and made a dash for the fish, but Pinky was too quick for her and managed to grab her just as she neared the funnel of the crab pot. He held her tight and told her it was a trap, but she was very hungry and really wanted some of that fish. Other crabs were rushing by and entering the crab pots.

Pinky and the sook watched as the other crabs fought over the fish until it was gone. Then the crabs tried to swim away, but to their surprise they ran into wire mesh at every turn. They were trapped. A few small ones did squeeze through the cull rings, but the big crabs were doomed. The sook shuddered as she snuggled

Watermen and their crab pots.

closer to Pinky, and he knew by the grateful look in her eyes that she would not be so eager to eat fresh fish the next time she had a chance.

But the sook was still hungry, and Pinky knew she needed nourishment to help her shell get hard and for the growth of her eggs, so they headed toward the bay.

Chapter 8: Pinky Gives the Slip to a Scrape

As Pinky and the sook reached the bay, they were still searching for food to eat before nightfall. They stayed fairly close to the shore among the other crabs and the strands of seaweed, where there was always an abundance of food. As they began to nibble on anything suitable for a crab's palate, they even forgot about each other.

As time passed and Pinky was beginning to feel satisfied, he looked around for his sook. Just as he spotted her, he noticed the water, grass, seahorses, oysters, and crabs all moving by so fast that he couldn't keep track of her. He darted away just as a scrape passed him and watched in dismay as his beloved sook was hauled to the surface. A waterman was scraping for peeler crabs, and Pinky had barely escaped, but was worried about his sook.

Suddenly, with a big splash, the scrape dropped back into the water, and as it settled to the bottom Pinky stayed behind it. He didn't know whether to flee or wait and see if the sook would reappear. Unbeknownst to him, the waterman was sorting his catch and keeping soft crabs, peelers, sooks, and Jimmy crabs. Pinky watched as the discards and debris returned to the bay bottom. The few crabs that were returned to the water were so frightened they swam away fast and never looked back.

Pinky decided that he too should flee from this dangerous place, and he reluctantly headed for deeper water, his eyes darting all around in search of his sook. Suddenly, as several crabs rushed past, he saw one that was bigger than the others and swam after it. His heart began to race as he recognized his sweetheart. As he pursued her, she never slowed down until she was in very deep water and near the bottom. At last she stopped to rest and Pinky caught up to her. She recognized

Pinky got away again!

23

him and immediately swam into his open arms. She had been lucky; since she was between too hard and too soft, the waterman had tossed her back.

As their fear slowly faded, the two grateful crabs wondered if there was anyplace, anywhere that was safe for crabs. They swam around until they found some discarded pieces of junk on the bottom and settled among them to rest. It had been an exhausting, frightening day, but a few hours of daylight still remained.

Pinky and the sook stayed close together for a few more days until they both knew she was strong and able to protect herself. As they parted, Pinky knew that like him, she too was a survivor because of her size. He knew she would go south and hibernate for the winter, and by next summer she would have released her eggs. He was content.

Pinky spent the rest of the summer dodging predators and watermen's traps. He learned to hang around the crab pots early in the morning as they were being fished and re-baited. He ate scraps of bait fish that fell from the pots, and sometimes he ate the dead crabs that fell with the old bait. He was becoming more sea-wise all the time.

Two watermen fish a gill net.

Chapter 9: Pinky Gets Away from a Gill Net

Just as Pinky was congratulating himself on recognizing all of the men's traps and knowing how to avoid them, he found that he was very much mistaken. He had swum right into a gill net. He didn't even see it until he was hopelessly entangled.

Is this gill netter just after fish, or is he keeping crabs as well?

He began to struggle frantically to free himself but the more he struggled, the more entangled he became.

Don't panic, he told himself. He relaxed and observed his situation. As he watched, more and more crabs and fish swam into the net and became entangled. They too struggled frantically, to no avail. Pinky thought this had to be the worst mess he'd been in for quite some time. He wondered if the waterman was after fish or crabs, since he was catching both. He also wondered whether he'd be set free if he even survived to be hauled aboard the boat.

After giving it a lot of thought, he decided he must free himself. He checked to see which of his parts were tangled in the net. His paddle fins were free, but one fin on each side was hopelessly entangled. His claws were just poking through the net and were somewhat caught. He carefully worked on the net with a sawing motion and managed to cut through and free his claws one at a time. He had to be careful not to get re-entangled as he tried to free his fins, but try as he might, he could not free them.

Pinky was a sea-wise crab. After all these years with no missing parts, he finally realized what he must do to survive. He detached himself from his entangled fins—after all, what were two fins compared to his life? He knew he'd grow two new fins the next time he shed. (Crabs are unique—they grow new appendages to replace missing ones each time they shed their shells in order to grow.) Pinky released his fins, which remained in the gill net, and he was finally free and backed away and then swam to the top of the water and over the net. As he neared the top he could see boats scattered across the bay. Watermen were everywhere!

Watermen were everywhere!

Pinky watched as the net came out of the water and onto the boat. He nearly got caught in the moving net but darted under the boat, which seemed to be the only safe place for the moment. He stayed under the boat until the net was all aboard and the boat began to speed up. As he was swimming back to where the net had been he noticed more nets full of crabs and fish. They appeared in every direction like a maze. Pinky very

26

carefully evaded them until he got close to the shoreline, where it was too shallow for boats or nets. There he dined and spent the night; he was a very weary crab.

At the crack of dawn, Pinky was on the move again. Constant moving, eating, and hiding is how crabs survive and become sea-wise. Watermen pursue them nearly all year with all kinds of contraptions. About the only time the watermen rest is during stormy weather. But even stormy weather is a threat to crabs, especially northeasters or hurricanes. Only a truly sea-wise crab like Pinky survives all that threatens.

At the crack of dawn, Pinky was on his way again.

Chapter 10: Pinky Goes into Hibernation

Pinky spent the rest of the summer and fall doing pretty much the same things he had in years past: hunting for food, enjoying an occasional romance, dodging predators and contraptions, and just surviving and becoming more sea-wise.

It was getting late in the year and time to head south for the winter. He decided to stay close to shore in hopes of reaching the mouth of the bay without losing any more parts or getting caught. It was a constant struggle to survive.

He diligently worked his way south as the weather turned colder and the water chilled. He stopped to mingle with other crabs along the way and offered advice to the younger ones about how to survive the harsh winter and how to become sea-wise such as he. Some thanked him for his concern, but others laughed and asked,

Even missing his fins, Pinky's still a romantic.

"If you're so wise, what happened to your missing fins?" He could tell, as he swam on, which ones would never survive to be Jimmy crabs.

When the time came to dig in for the winter, Pinky tried to find a place away from so many other crabs, but once he buried himself in the muddy bottom, other crabs settled in all around him. His thoughts turned to the sook, and he wondered if she was nearby.

Pinky knew from previous years that soon watermen would come with dredges to seek the crabs out. A crab couldn't even do what comes naturally and hibernate without fear. The watermen just never quit!

Pinky's out there somewhere, hibernating until spring comes.

29

Crabs have a hard time surviving the winter. When they go dormant, they get so cold that they can't scurry away as fast as they can when it's warm. Even if they see a dredge coming, they can't move fast enough to escape. Sometimes the teeth of the dredge cut right into them and kill or maim them.

This was really Pinky's biggest worry, because it meant that his survival was more or less out of his control. He hoped he'd be lucky and the dredges would miss him as they had in years past. With that thought, Pinky came out of the mud and moved away from the mass of crabs snuggled around him. He headed for an area closer to the Chesapeake Bay Bridge-Tunnel.

Pinky remembered the year before, when he was close to the tunnel and he and the other crabs buried near him all survived with no disturbance whatsoever. The watermen never brought their boats close to the bridge. Only a sea-wise crab would remember such an important detail.

With that last thought Pinky, the sea-wise crab, settled down deep in the mud for the long, cold winter, confident he'd survive 'til spring when his struggle would continue.

Will Pinky survive near the Chesapeake Bay Bridge-Tunnel?

The crab lady often remembers Pinky as she works and likes to think he still survives.

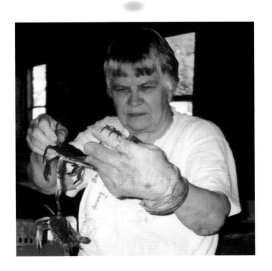

The story of Pinky is based on an actual crab, and the part of the story leading to his release is true. Hopefully what Judy imagines to be his trials and tribulations will encourage all who read it to have more compassion and respect for all living things. We're all just trying to survive.

Glossary of Crab Terms

BUSTER CRAB   A crab whose shell has cracked and is in the process of shedding.

CRAB POT   A wire mesh cage approximately 24 inches square with funnels on the sides, at the bottom. Once crabs enter the funnels, they can't get out and are trapped in the upper part of the pot.

CRAB TRAP   A wire mesh fence leading from shallow water near shore to a large cage trap in deep water. The fence leads to the only opening in the cage, a narrowing funnel that crabs can't escape.

CULL   To sort crabs and throw back those that are too small or not in the correct stage.

CULL RING   A round opening in the side of a crab pot or trap that permits crabs that are under the legal size to escape unharmed.

DOUBLER CRAB   A male crab holding a female who is about to shed and become a sook, in hopes of mating when she becomes a soft crab.

DREDGE   Similar to a scrape except much larger and with steel teeth that dig into the bottom to extract crabs that have buried themselves to hibernate.

FLOAT or SHEDDING TANK   Boxes approximately 4 feet wide, 8 feet long, and 10 inches deep that allow a constant exchange of salt water; used for keeping peeler crabs until they have shed and become soft crabs.

GILL NET   Fishing nets that are hung vertically in a body of water to catch fish by their gills.

JIMMY CRAB   An adult male crab—also called a "hard crab."

OYSTER TOAD   An ugly, lumpy fish with a big mouth and teeth.

PEELER   A crab in shedding cycle prior to becoming a buster crab.

SCRAPE   A steel frame with net bag attached that lies flat on the bottom of the bay. It is pulled by boat to scrape crabs from the bottom into the net and then hauled aboard the boat and dumped into the cull box.

SHE-CRAB   A juvenile female—not mature enough for mating.

SOOK   A full-grown female, ready to mate and lay eggs.

SHED or MOLT   To cast off a shell in order to grow larger.

SOFT CRAB   Any crab, male or female, immediately after shedding its shell.

WATERMEN   Commercial fishermen who fish the waters of the Chesapeake Bay and its tributaries.

Boat with a dredge rig.